Illustrated by Art Mawhinney

pi phoenix international publications, inc.
kids

It's the day of the big Boonta Eve Podrace on Tatooine! Sebulba is the favorite, but young Anakin Skywalker zooms ahead.

While Anakin makes his move, search the scene for these racers and their fans:

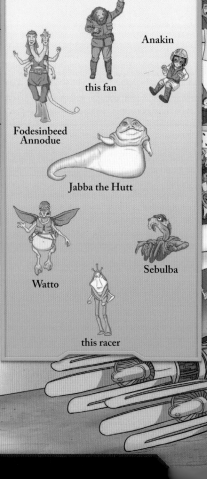

Anakin

this fan

Fodesinbeed Annodue

Jabba the Hutt

Watto

Sebulba

this racer

Senator Amidala has been attacked! The brave Jedi Knights Anakin Skywalker and Obi-Wan Kenobi chase the senator's attacker through the skies of Coruscant.

Help the Jedi Knights search for the assassin and these other flying things:

GALAXIES OPERA

DEX'S

Supreme Chancellor Palpatine has been captured by the evil General Grievous! Obi-Wan Kenobi and Anakin Skywalker must blast their way through a blockade of spaceships to save the Supreme Chancellor.

First find the Jedi Knights, then help them avoid enemy fire by spotting these ships:

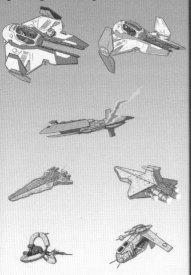

The evil Empire has taken over the galaxy. Luckily, the rebels have a new hope—Luke Skywalker. Now they just need a spaceship!

Search the Cantina on Tatooine for these pirates, smugglers, and other ne'er-do-wells. Is one of them the pilot Luke is looking for?

Greedo

Han Solo

this musician

Chewbacca

this customer

this smuggler

this alien

Han, Chewie, and Princess Leia need somewhere to hide from the evil Darth Vader. Cloud City, run by Han's old friend Lando Calrissian, seems like the perfect place!

But something isn't right for our heroes. Search the scene for these hidden menaces:

Han Solo is in the clutches of the slimy gangster Jabba the Hutt. Luckily Han has powerful friends. Luke Skywalker has a message for Jabba—free Han, or else!

While Jabba considers Luke's offer, search Jabba's shindig for these party guests:

this bounty hunter

this party guest

Chewbacca

Han Solo

Boba Fett

Luke Skywalker

this party guest

Salacious B. Crumb

Years after the battle of Endor, the distant desert planet Jakku is filled with wrecked ships, busted droids, and other junk. But if you look hard enough, you might just find something great!

Scavenge the desert for all these things:

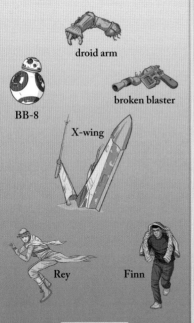

droid arm

BB-8

broken blaster

X-wing

Rey

Finn

Rey is a skilled desert scavenger. She looks through old junk and finds good, usable parts.

As Rey trades in her latest haul for something to eat, look around the trading post for these food-related items:

Most spectators put their credits on Sebulba to win, but Anakin has his supporters. Hurry back to the podrace and find fans holding signs that spell A-N-A-K-I-N!

There's plenty to do on Coruscant. Go back to the big city and search for these places:

the Galaxies Opera House

Dex's Diner

the Snapping Septoid

the Vos Gesal Hotel

the Outlander Club

Return to the battle against General Grievous and search for 10 buzz droids, like these:

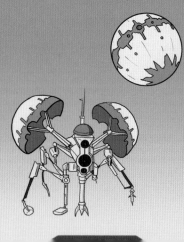

Droids aren't allowed in the Cantina, but some snuck in! Go back to the Cantina and find them. These are the droids you're looking for:

Go back to Cloud City and search the skies for clouds that look like:

Yoda

Darth Vader

a lightsaber

C-3PO

R2-D2

Dance back to Jabba's palace party to find these members of the Max Rebo Band:

Sy Snootles

Ak-rev

Joh Yowza

Lyn Me

Max Rebo

Rystáll Sant

The Jakku desert is a rough place to live, but it's perfect for *some*. Head back to Jakku to find these desert dwellers:

Need a snack? Travel back to the Trading Post on Jakku and trade in these items for some food: